Sugar

by Rhoda Nottridge

Wayland

Additives
Vitamins
Fibre
Sugar
Fats
Proteins

Words printed in **bold** can be found in the glossary on page 30.

First published in 1992 by Wayland (Publishers) Ltd.
61 Western Road, Hove, East Sussex, BN3 1JD

British Library Cataloguing in Publication Data

Nottridge, Rhoda
 Sugar – (Food Facts Series)
 I. Title II. Jackson, Maureen
 III. Yates, John IV. Series
 641.3
 ISBN 0 7502 0358 7

Series Editor: Kathryn Smith
Designer: Helen White
Artwork: John Yates
Cartoons: Maureen Jackson

Typesetting by White Design
Printed and bound in Belgium by Casterman S.A.

Contents

Spotting sugar 4

Growing sugar 9

The sugar factory 12

Refined sugar 15

The history of sugar 19

Sugar and health 23

Sweeteners today 26

Glossary 30

Books to read 31

Index 32

Spotting sugar

Sugar can be a wonderful source of energy but it can also be bad for our health. To understand how sugar can be both these things we need to find out what it is and what it does to our bodies.

We have all seen the type of sugar which we find in a bowl at home or in a café. This kind of sugar is called **refined** sugar. It is made out of one of two plants; either sugar beet or sugar cane.

There are lots of different kinds of refined sugar, such as white sugar lumps or soft, brown sugar. We add these kinds of sugar to our food to make it taste sweeter. We do not always need or want to add sugar to our food. Many people like sweet-tasting foods and fortunately some foods such as fruit contain sugar already, so we do not need to add more.

Did you know that sometimes we can eat sugar and not even know it? Sugar is often added at food factories to prepared foods and drinks. It helps to stop them from going **mouldy**.

ABOVE We eat sugar everyday without even noticing. Many favourite foods such as ice-cream contain sugar.

We may not notice that a food contains sugar. Baked beans, tomato ketchup and other savoury foods often contain a lot of sugar which has been specially added.

We need to find out which foods contain sugar because we may be eating more of it than we realize. We need to become sugar spotters to stay fit and healthy.

The sugar family

There are several types of sugar in the sugar family. They all make things taste sweet but they don't all come from the same plants or parts of plants.

BELOW Look at the ingredient label on the side of your favourite canned drink. The word sugar or glucose will probably appear on it. Checking ingredient labels is an easy way to start spotting the sugar in your diet.

Sugar is the name we generally give to the type of sugar called *sucrose*. Sucrose is extracted from sugar beet and sugar cane. It is a mixture of glucose and fructose.

Fructose is the sweetener that occurs naturally in fruit and it is the main type of sugar in honey. Fruit and vegetables are the main sources of *glucose*. Partially-cooked cereals contain *maltose* whilst the sugar that is found in milk and other dairy foods is known as *lactose*.

What is sweetness?

There are around 100 different things which make foods taste sweet. We do not know why we like sweet tastes but most people do and so do some animals. Children tend to like sweet tastes even more than adults.

We taste sweetness with some of our taste buds. A sweet taste is only recognized by the taste buds on the tip of our tongue. Try this experiment.

Stick out your tongue and place a sugar lump at the side of your tongue. You probably cannot taste the sweetness. Wash out your mouth. Now put a sugar lump on the tip of your tongue. You will be able to taste the sugar.

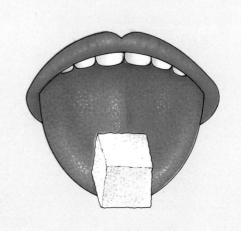

Sugar in plants

All green plants contain sugar, although they may not always taste sweet. However, some parts of plants which contain a lot of sugar, such as their fruit, do usually taste sweet. Others have sweet roots, such as parsnips.

Plants need sugar to live and grow. They store it and use it when they need energy. The sweetness of fruit also attracts birds and other animals. These animals eat the fruit and the seeds of the plant are passed into their stomachs and come out in the animals' droppings. The animals get energy from the sugar in the fruit and seeds are left scattered around the countryside, so that new plants can grow where the seeds have been left.

Green plants make their sugar stores by mixing together some of nature's most important materials. The plants' leaves **absorb** sunlight and a part of the air that we breathe which is called carbon dioxide. The plants absorb water in the soil through their roots. Then by mixing the carbon dioxide, sun, water and chlorophyll (the substance in plants which makes them green), the plants make sugar.

BELOW This fruit bat is dining on wild figs. Unlike humans, animals get all the sugar they need in its natural form from plants and fruit.

Most plants don't make very much sugar, so it is only noticeable in their fruit. There are two plants which are a little different. They make and store a lot of sugar. These plants are called sugar beet and sugar cane. We use them to make the sugar we eat.

Spot that sugar!

1. Carefully read the ingredients labels on your favourite savoury canned or packet foods and your favourite drinks.

2. Do the ingredients include sugar?

3. If the ingredients don't include sugar, see if the words *sucrose*, *fructose*, *glucose*, *maltose* or *lactose* are listed. These mean sugar too!

4. Make a list of all the food and drinks you find that you think taste savoury but have discovered include sugar.

Food	Sweet or Savoury	Does it contain sugar?
Hot Dog Sausages	Savoury	Sugar
Fizzy Drink (Orange)	Sweet	Glucose

Growing sugar

Sugar cane

Sugar cane is a very tall grass which grows in hot, sunny countries where there is also plenty of rainfall. The canes have long, golden stalks which grow up to 5 m high.

The plant stores its sugar supply inside the stalk. In some countries you can buy chunks of sugar cane to eat. You can taste the sugar as you suck the cane. It tastes very sweet!

Sugar cane can be harvested at any time when the ground is dry and the farmer has decided the canes are big enough to contain a large store of sugar.

The canes used to be cut down by people one by one, which was very hard work in the hot sun. Nowadays machines are usually used to do the hard work of cutting down the canes.

The roots of the canes are left in the ground and the next year, new shoots start to grow from the old roots.

RIGHT The sugar cane plant stores its sugar in the thick cane. At this stage the sugar is very different from the sugar we use every day.

9

Sugar beet

Sugar beet is the other main plant that we use for sugar. However, it stores sugar in its roots, not in a stalk. Like a potato or carrot, it is called a root vegetable because the part that tastes good to eat is the root that grows underground.

New beet plants are grown by the farmer from seeds.

BELOW When the sugar beet is harvested the green leafy tops which grow above the soil are cut off and used for animal feed.

These seeds come from special beet plants which have been left until their second year to flower and produce seeds.

Sugar beet grows well in countries where it is warm in the summer but cool or cold in the winter. So it is farmed in places like Europe, the USA, Canada, China and Japan. Most sugar used in Europe comes from sugar beet.

Investigation

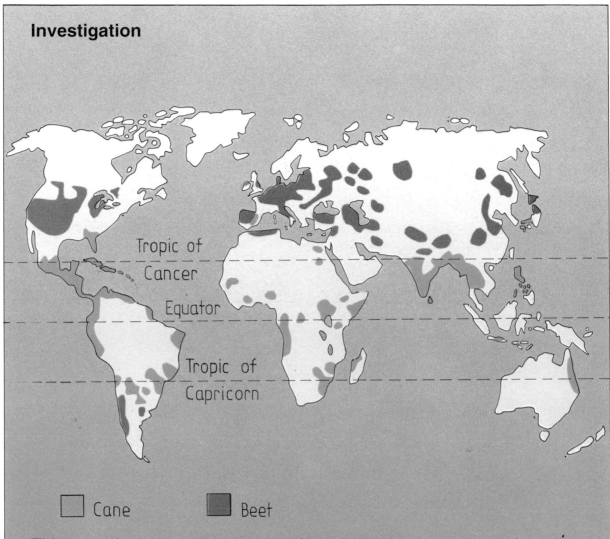

☐ Cane   ■ Beet

This map shows you some of the places where sugar cane and sugar beet are grown in the world. Altogether, nearly 100 million tonnes of sugar are produced every year. Over half of this comes from sugar cane and the rest from sugar beet.

Most sugar cane is grown in the nine countries listed below. Do you know where each country is on the map? Use an atlas to help you find the countries.

Australia Brazil China Cuba India Mexico Philippines Thailand USA

The sugar factory

ABOVE Modern sugar mills, such as this one in South Africa, process thousands of tonnes of sugar cane or beet every day.

To get all the sugar out of beet and cane it has to be taken from the farms where it grows to a factory. In the factory it is changed from being a natural plant into the kind of crystals that we know as sugar.

Sugar cane is quite tough on the outside so it has to be cut up into small pieces and then the juice is washed out of the canes. Another way to get the juice out is by squeezing the canes through huge **rolling mills**. The bits of squashed cane which are left over are used as fuel or made into a **pulp** which is used to make paper.

Sugar beet is washed and sliced by machines into small strips. Sugar dissolves in water, which is why we add it to drinks such as tea and coffee.

To get all the sugar out of the beet strips, they are soaked in hot water so that the sugar will dissolve into the water. The sugar from the cane is also dissolved into huge tanks containing water.

The sugar solution is a muddy, dark colour and has to be made more pure. It is poured into tanks where it is mixed up with a **chemical** called lime. The lime separates the sugar from any other bits so that all that is left is a pure **solution** of sugar.

In a special boiler the sugar solution is heated. It becomes so hot that most of the water **evaporates**. What is left is a sugary syrup.

The syrup then has to be turned into sugar crystals. Crystals will grow when they are attached to other crystals. To make sugar crystals, some crystals which have already been grown are put into the syrup and this helps new crystals to form.

BELOW The sugar-making process produces many different types of white and brown sugars and syrups. This small selection shows only a few of the sugar products on sale in super-markets today.

The crystals then have to be separated from the liquid by rotating the mixture in a huge drum. A syrup, called molasses, is drained off.

Refining sugar

The sugar crystals that come out of the huge spinning drums still have a fine coating of molasses on them. These large, dark brown crystals are called demerara sugar, named after the town in Guyana, South America where demerara sugar was first made.

The sugar then goes to another factory where it is refined, which means that it is made even purer. The sugar is soaked in a thick, syrupy mixture. This mixture is so sugary already that it cannot dissolve any more sugar or make any more sugar crystals. This means it is saturated. The coating of molasses comes off the crystals and sticks to the syrup. Then the crystals and syrup are spun round together which separates them.

The crystals are dissolved in water and are then allowed to form into crystals again. This time, the crystals are much smaller and we end up with the pure, white refined sugar which we have all seen in shops.

Making a saturated solution

Sugar crystals dissolve in water and make a sugary solution. However, there comes a point when so much sugar has dissolved in the water that no more can dissolve in it. No matter how hard you try, you will not be able to dissolve any more crystals. This is called a saturated solution. This is the kind of solution that is used to remove the molasses from the sugar crystals when sugar is being refined.

1. Fill a glass half full with warm water.
2. Drop in a very small pinch of granulated white sugar crystals.
3. Stir the solution quite hard until all the crystals have dissolved.
4. Keep adding crystals, a few at a time. Eventually, the crystals will not dissolve any more and will stay at the bottom of the glass. The solution is saturated.

Refined sugar

Problems with refined sugar

Molasses contains a small amount of some **vitamins**, **minerals** and other substances which are good for us. Unfortunately refining sugar takes out all the goodness, so that there are no vitamins or minerals left in white sugar. If you use sugar it is better to choose a brown sugar which has not been refined much, because it will still contain some molasses.

BELOW Some people become addicted to eating sugary products such as chocolates, and experience strong cravings for them.

There is a further problem with refined sugar (sucrose). The factory has already done the hard work of making the sugar pure. When we eat sucrose, our **digestive systems** do not bother working properly because it is so refined. The sucrose goes straight into our blood. This gives us energy very fast.

This may sound like a good thing but when we have used up the sugar our energy level

drops very quickly. We feel tired and the only way to get more energy is to eat more sugar. So we eat more sugar and then our energy levels rise and fall even more. We can end up eating more and more sugar and getting cravings for sweet things to top up our energy levels. Our digestive system stops working properly, too. Because sucrose goes straight into our blood, our digestion system does not have time to absorb other important foods that may be mixed up with the sugar.

These problems only happen with sucrose. The sugars in foods like fruit or honey have not been refined so our digestive systems work properly when we eat them.

ABOVE Drinking sugar-free or 'diet' drinks is a good way of cutting out extra sugar.

Types of refined sugar

White Sugars

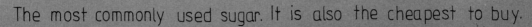

Granulated white sugar

The most commonly used sugar. It is also the cheapest to buy.

Cube sugar

This is made from granulated sugar that has been dampened and then moulded into cube shapes.

Caster sugar

It is like granulated sugar but the crystals are smaller and dissolve more easily. It is often used when baking.

Icing sugar

To make icing sugar, the sugar crystals are ground into a fine powder. This dissolves quickly with water to make a paste that can be used for decorating cakes.

Preserving sugar

This is used for making jam. It has large crystals which dissolve very slowly. Because jam has to be heated for a long time the bottom of the saucepan would burn if the crystals dissolve too fast.

Brown sugars
There are lots of different types of brown sugar, which vary in colour depending on how much molasses has been added to them. These sugars are used to sweeten coffee and sometimes in baking, when a stronger taste is wanted.

Demerara
This used to be the large raw sugar crystals but nowadays it is white sugar which has had molasses added back to it.

Treacle and molasses
These are dark brown liquids which separate from the sugar crystals in the factory. They are used in baking when a strong taste is wanted.

Syrups
Some of the sugar solutions left over from refining sugar cane or beet can be made into golden syrups. There is also another kind of syrup, which comes from the sap of a maple tree. This is called maple syrup. Other sugary syrups are made from vegetables such as corn.

The history of sugar

The exact history of sugar cane, the first known source of sugar, is not clear. It probably grew wild in the Polynesian Islands, far out in the Pacific Ocean. From there, the magical sugar cane somehow came to be grown in India and China, along with the secret of how to get the sweetness from it. Stories grew around the sugar cane. In India, a king called Subandu is said to have found sugar cane growing in his bedroom. The sugar cane was said to have produced a prince called IIshvaku.

LEFT In the past sugar, and the things made from it, were a luxury for the wealthy. Today many products made from sugar, like these sweets, can be bought for just a few pence.

The secret of sugar cane

The history of sugar is a fascinating tale of a food which has brought fabulous wealth to some and great unhappiness and suffering to others.

In 510 BC, people from Persia, now called Iran, invaded India and discovered the tall canes growing there. They were delighted with this wonderful plant that gave 'honey without bees'. They took plants to Persia and over hundreds of years they became the most skilled growers and makers of sugar, jealously guarding the secret of the canes.

About 100 years later, Alexander the Great conquered the **continent** of Asia and began growing sugar and selling it. The Alexandrians even added colourings to their sugar to make it more tempting to buy. They crushed sea snails, insects and herb roots to colour the sugar violet or pink. The ancient Greeks and Romans used it as a luxury and a medicine.

The popularity of sugar spread rapidly. Sugar cane was grown in Egypt, Cyprus, Rhodes, North Africa, southern Spain and Syria. By the tenth century, ships loaded with sugar sailed across the Mediterranean Sea to sell the new luxury to **Venetian** merchants.

It was in 1099 that sugar finally travelled as far as Britain. Some British

crusaders travelling in Syria came across what they called the new 'spice'. They eagerly brought it back to Britain, selling it at around seventy times today's prices!

Sugar and slavery
By the fifteenth century the explorer Christopher Columbus had taken sugar cane to the West Indies to see how it would grow. To his delight, he discovered that this was the perfect place for growing sugar, with just the right amount of rain and sun. Europeans began to experiment with growing sugar cane in other countries too, such as Brazil, Cuba and Mexico.

ABOVE In the early days of sugar production people from Africa were taken away from their homes and country and forced to work as slaves in the sugar factories, in what were often terrible conditions.

ABOVE These days sugar cane and beet is not usually harvested by hand. It is cut by efficient machines, such as the one being used in this picture.

their countries. They were chained up and forced on to ships travelling to places like the West Indies. Many died on the journey and many more died as slaves working on the plantations.

At that time there were no machines to make the work easier. The slaves worked in dreadful conditions under the burning sun, cutting down the canes by hand. The Europeans grew richer.

Dutch and French explorers travelling in the Indian Ocean made sugar **plantations** in Indonesia, the Philippines and Hawaii.

Soon, planting and developing vast sugar plantations in these countries had become a way of becoming fabulously wealthy. Sugar cane became known as white gold.

However, these sugar plantations succeeded only because of the efforts of the slaves who were forced to work for the plantation owners. Behind the glamorous wealth of the owners was a terrible story. To find people to work on the plantations, the Europeans turned to Africa. People were torn away from their homes, their villages and

The sugar beet story

Sugar beet had been eaten as a vegetable as far back as Roman times but it was not until 1812 that a good method was found of getting the sugar out of the beet plant.

The French and the British had been at war for some time. The British took control of the seas and stopped the French from bringing in more sugar. Napoleon, the French leader, encouraged the French to grow sugar beet so that they would no longer have to rely on sugar cane.

By 1880, sugar beet had become the main source of sugar in Europe and its growth had spread to many other countries, such as the USA and Canada.

Sugar and health

If you eat a lot of sugar it will harm your health. There are two very important reasons for not eating too much sugar. The first reason is that sugar will harm your teeth.

BELOW It is better for our health to eat food containing sugar in its natural form. A crunchy apple makes a tasty snack and is much better for us than sweets.

There are tiny germs which live in our mouths called **bacteria**. They feed on sugar and turn it into a sticky layer on our teeth called **plaque**.

The plaque slowly builds up between our teeth and sticks to the bottom of each tooth, round the gum. The plaque softens the layer of enamel which protects the teeth and so the teeth start to decay. If you do not get rid of the plaque completely it forms a hard layer which has to be scraped off by the dentist.

The best way to avoid tooth decay is by not eating and drinking sugary things. Brushing teeth regularly will help to get rid of plaque. It is also important to get your teeth checked regularly by a dentist.

The other main problem with eating too many sugary foods is that people can become over-weight. Some put on a lot of weight because they eat too much sugar and do not exercise. Their bodies have no way of using up all the extra energy the sugar has given them. So the body stores the energy as fat. This can lead to serious illnesses such as heart disease or even heart failure.

Some people suffer from an illness called **diabetes** which means they have too much sugar in their blood supply. For them, eating sugar is dangerous. They have to be very careful and avoid sugar in what they eat.

Cutting down on sugar

It is worth getting into the habit of thinking about how much sugar you have in your food. You do not need to worry if you eat sugary things every now and then but try to change some of your everyday eating habits. There are many ways of cutting down on the amount of sugar in your diet.

Why not choose unsweetened fruit juices and drink these diluted with water. An ordinary soft drink contains around 5 teaspoonfuls of sugar!

Checking your teeth for plaque

Normally, we cannot see plaque easily because it is colourless. But **disclosing tablets**, which you can buy at the chemist, can help you to see it. Chew one of these tablets. It will turn bits of your teeth bright pink! The pink bits are to show you where you have plaque. Then you can brush off the pink bits and you will be brushing away the plaque. Chew a second disclosing tablet when you have cleaned your teeth. Are there any pink spots left? If there are, clean your teeth again to remove the last bits of plaque.

Remember, though, that it is best to avoid having plaque by eating fewer sugary food and drinks.

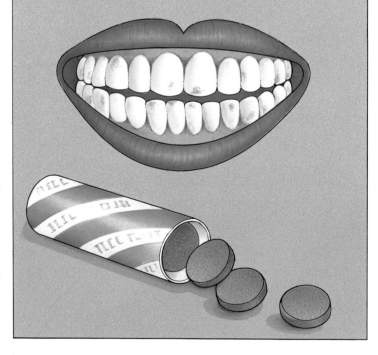

If you drink tea or coffee, slowly cut out added sugar. They actually taste more refreshing without sugar. Check that the breakfast cereal you eat does not have added sugar. Some cereals contain so much sugar that they are half sugar and half cereal. Try to find a cereal that does not contain any sugar and see if you can persuade all your family to change to it.

Cutting down on sugar also means choosing snacks which contain very little sugar and eating fewer sugary sweets. You can eat plenty of fresh fruit, vegetables, crackers, milk, natural yoghurt or nuts instead. You can even buy sugar-free sweets.

BELOW You can naturally sweeten your breakfast cereal with chopped fruit, such as bananas and strawberries, instead of using refined sugar.

Sweeteners today

There are other kinds of sweeteners apart from sugar that we can use. Nowadays a lot of people use **artificial sweeteners** such as saccharin. These kind of sweeteners are very popular in drinks. If you look at the label of a 'diet' drink, you will see that the drink contains an artificial sweetener. These sweeteners are made from chemicals, and have been invented quite recently. We do not yet know if they have any bad effects on the human body because they have not been around long enough for us to test them properly.

Honey is probably the oldest source of sweetness known to humans. It is the sweet, thick liquid made by bees. It is a good source of energy containing fructose and glucose.

RIGHT
For thousands of years honey from honeycomb has been used as a natural way to sweeten food.

Our bodies can digest fructose and glucose better than sucrose. Honey contains several other things which are good for us.

To make honey, bees sip at nectar, which is the liquid obtained at the centre of a flower. The bees then carry this nectar in a pouch back to their hive, which is the place where they live. They store the nectar in part of the hive, where the water in the nectar evaporates. What is left turns into honey.

Honey is an unrefined type of sugar and for this reason if we like things to taste sweet it is probably a good idea to use honey instead of sugar or an artificial sweetener.

ABOVE This honey bee is filling its pouch with nectar from the centre of a flower. The bee will return to the hive and store the nectar in the honeycomb.

Recipe

Next time you want to have a sweet dessert, try to avoid using sugar.
Here is a recipe for Yoghurt Snow. It makes a delicious topping for
fruit salad.

You will need:
2 egg whites
3 tablespoons of clear honey
300 g of natural yoghurt

1. Carefully separate the egg whites from the egg yolk.
2. Whisk the egg white until it is stiff.
3. Slowly add the honey and continue to whisk until the mixture is stiff.
4. Carefully fold in the yoghurt and stir all together.
5. Serve as a topping for fruit salad or any other dessert.

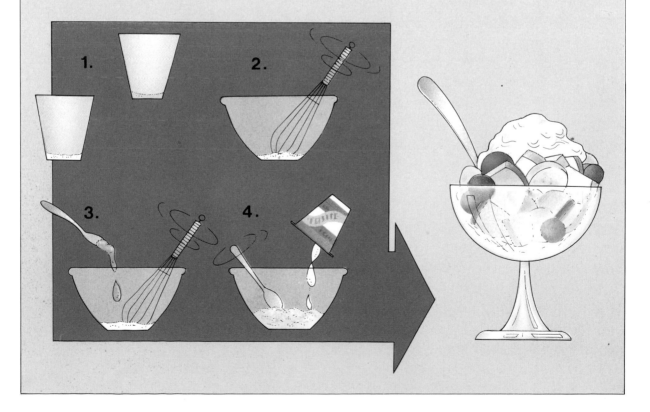

Glossary

Absorb   To soak up or take in.
Artificial sweeteners Substances that have been made to taste sweet.
Bacteria   Germs that may cause disease.
Chemical   A particular substance.
Climates   The weather conditions of a region.
Continent   A large land mass such as Africa or Australia.
Crusaders   Christian soldiers from Europe, who travelled to the Holy Land in medieval times.
Diabetes   An illness which means that a person's body cannot cope with sugar.
Digestion   When the body dissolves food in the stomach so that it can get energy out of it.
Digestive system   The parts of our body that take the goodness out of food.
Disclosing tablets   Special tablets which show up plaque on teeth.
Evaporates   When liquid is lost because it changes into vapour.
Minerals   Substances found in some foods which our bodies need to function properly.
Mouldy   When a food becomes stale and fungus starts to grow on the surface of it.
Plantation   A large farm, usually in hot countries, where one crop is grown for money.
Plaque A sticky layer on the teeth which comes from sugar and bacteria.
Pulp   A soft, soggy mixture of part of the sugar cane and water. It can be used to make paper.
Refined   To make something finer or purer.
Rolling mills Large cylinders which roll together, to crush or flatten anything fed between them.
Sap   A liquid in plants which is partially made of sugar.
Solution   A liquid with something dissolved in it.
Tropical   Areas of the world where the weather is very hot, usually with a lot of rainfall.
Venetian   People from the city of Venice in Italy.
Vitamins   Substances found in food that your body needs to remain healthy.

Books to read

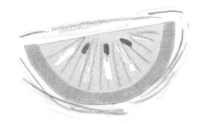

A Spoonful of Sugar by D. A. Lucas (Wayland, 1985)

Healthy Teeth by Constance Milburn (Wayland, 1990)

Focus on Sugar by Alan Blackwood (Wayland, 1985)

Sugar by Rhoda Nottridge (Wayland, 1989)

Your Teeth by J. Iveson-Iveson (Wayland, 1982)

Picture Acknowledgements

Aspect 10; Cephas 15; Chapel Studios *Cover*,13, 25; Bruce Coleman 7, 12, 22, 28; Mary Evans 21; Jeff Greenberg 16, 27; Tony Stone 19; Zefa 4, 5, 8, 9, 23.

Index

Africa   20, 22
Asia   20
Australia   11

bacteria   23
blood   15, 16,2 4
Brazil   11, 22
Britain   20, 21, 22

Canada   10, 22
carbon dioxide   7
China   10, 11, 19
Columbus, Christopher 21
Cuba   11, 22
Cyprus   20

diabetes   24
diet   24
digestive system 15, 16, 28

Egypt   20
energy   4, 6, 15, 16, 24
Europe   10, 21, 22

France   22
fructose   5, 8, 26
fruit   4, 5, 6, 7, 16, 25
 juice 24

glucose   5, 8, 26

health   4, 5, 23, 24

Holland   22
honey   5, 16, 20, 26, 28, 29

India   11, 19, 20
Indian Ocean   22
Indonesia   22
Iran   20

Japan   10

lactose   5, 8
lime   13

maltose   5, 8
Mexico   11, 22
minerals   15
molasses   13, 14, 15, 18
mould   4

Napoleon   22

Pacific Ocean   19
Philippines   11
plaque   23, 24

Rhodes   20

saccharin   26
Spain   20
sugar
 beet   4, 5, 7, 10, 11, 13, 22
 brown   4, 13, 15, 18

cane   4, 5, 7, 9, 11, 13, 19, 20, 22
caster   17
crystals   12, 13, 14, 18
cubes   17
demerara   13, 18
icing   17
preserving   17
refined   4, 13, 14, 15, 16, 17, 18
white 4,14,15,17,18
Syria   20, 21
syrup   13, 14, 18
 golden   18
 maple   18

tastebuds   6
Thailand   11
tooth decay   23, 24
treacle   18

USA   10, 11, 22
USSR   10

vegetables   25
vitamins   15

West Indies   21, 22